Hello, Stupid!

by

A. L. Kitselman

Originally published as
Hello, Stupid!
by The Translator's Press
5455 LA Jolla Boulevard
La Jolla,
California
U.S.A.
Copyright 1962 by A.L. Kitselman

New edition published in the USA and the UK
by

MASTERWORKS INTERNATIONAL
27 Old Gloucester Street
London
WC1N 3XX
UK

Email: admin@mwipublishing.com
Web: http:/www.mwipublishing.com

ISBN: 978-0-9933465-3-8
copyright © A. L. Kitselman 1962, 2017

Cover by mwidesign.com
Male Figure: ? head 4 © Chrisharvey/Dreamstime

CONTENTS

Foreward to the New Edition

This republication of the book "Hello, Stupid!" by A. L. Kitselman (1914-1980) is the final volume of the *Kitselman Collection*. This collection of six books represents a unique record of the thoughts of this extraordinary figure. Beau, as he was affectionately known to family and friends, was a true renaissance man, a polymath. His interests ranged from mathematics, physics and early computer programming to Eastern philosophy and lost languages.

This, his final book, published in 1962, is an extraordinary challenge to modern scientific research and government. It was written shortly after the "Bay of Pigs" incident when the world came to the brink of nuclear war and the fears of another global conflict, a World War III, were at an all-time high. *Hello, Stupid!* continues with themes that Beau had touched upon in his fictional book "The Fuse."[1] Fundamentally, since 1936 Beau had been concerned with the possibilities for the transformation of human consciousness through a process he called 'integration.' In his later life, his emphasis had begun to the transformation of society as a whole, particularly in the realms of science and government.

Much of the book is in the form of an imagined dialogue in which Kitselman answers questions, argues and provokes to deepen the reader's understanding of all the issues explored throughout. As in many of his books Kitselman used his own handwriting instead of normal typesetting. In this reproduction Kitselman's own voice is set in a script style font and the other person's voice uses a normal serif style font .

In the book's first section, entitled "Space and Peace", he explores the whole issue of vested interests on modern scientific research. Vested interests not just in terms of finance but also the investment of scientists in both their position and prestige as well as their ideologies. He delves deeply into the experience of his best friend, the physicist Thomas Townsend Brown, whom he refers to in the text as B or commander B. Whilst T.T. Brown is perhaps best known for his work on the 'Biefeld Brown Effect' his interests and research covered a huge area.

> "Brown was blessed with the unique ability to "see what others have seen and think what nobody has thought." As a teenager in the 1920s, working in a well-equipped laboratory in the basement of his prominent Ohio family's opulent home, Brown noticed an unusual effect when high voltage was applied to a Coolidge X-Ray tube. With that observation, he came to believe he had discovered a link between electricity and gravity - and a way to lift and propel flying vehicles by purely electrical means.
>
> Thus begins the odyssey of T. Townsend Brown, who spent a lifetime crisscrossing the hemisphere in the relentless pursuit of his "flying saucer pipe dreams."
>
> From the "The Thomas Townsend Brown Family Website." [2]

At the time when Kitselman wrote this book, he and many other people felt that space exploration offered a real hope for the future of mankind, particularly if it could be done, both cost effectively and safely, through the use of new and innovative technologies.
In the second section of the book Kitselman offers some unique perspectives on his forte, the science of mathematics.

He castigates the whole field for a lack of scientific rigor and intellectual laziness.

In the last part of the book he explores the nature of all modern governments outlining their weaknesses and offering some possibilities for a new form of government.

Although "Hello, Stupid!" was first published some 55 years ago, it is still deeply relevant to this day (2017). Fears of atomic war may have receded but they have been replaced by global terrorism as a major personal, societal and political concern. Scientific research is now even more heavily influenced by the vested interests that Kitselman outlined back in the 1960s. Governments still govern poorly and many so-called democracies are being run by dictators thinly disguised as Presidents and First or Prime Ministers.

The Publishers

Footnotes:
1. The Fuse, isbn: 978-0-9927706-9-3, published by MWI 2015
2. http://www.thomastownsendbrown.com

HELLO, STUPID!

CAUTION

Do not read this book unless you are able to benefit from feeling 'stupid'. No one is trying to entertain you or produce a work of art or make money in these pages.

If you feel that the world is a mess, and that perhaps you, too, are a mess — welcome! This book is an <u>emetic</u>, for sick people in a sick world, capable of making you vomit forth your stupidities — that is, if you can get it 'down'.

Can you bear to be presented with proof that almost every trouble in the world today is your fault? If you can, these pages are for you and the few others like you.

On the other hand, if you feel, as most do, that 'they' (the people who 'run' things) are the trouble-makers of the world, kindly do not trespass here. This is not written for you, and I prefer to have nothing to do with you!

A. L. Kitselman

SPACE AND PEACE

I am so worried about the international situation. If only someone could find an easy, inexpensive way to get into space, then, instead of war, we might have twenty or thirty years of competitive space exploration and colonization! And in that length of time, we might even learn to get along with each other!

Near the end of the second decade of this present century, a teen-age amateur scientist discovered one 'easy, inexpensive way to get into space' (there are others); since that time his discovery has been a scientific jewel mounted in a setting of purest stupidity.

As this is a matter which may concern the lives of all of us, being interwoven with world peace, I will tell the story in some detail.

The son of a well-to-do family in eastern Ohio, young Mr. B. dreams of going into space (as most boys do now). Gradually he became convinced that he would find out how to do it.

The most mysterious force that young B. had heard of was the 'x'-ray, something which sounded far more mysterious then than it does now. He wondered if x-rays might be the key to space-travel, so he acquired a Coolidge x-ray tube and mounted it in careful balance, as if it were an astronomical telescope. His idea was to point the tube in different directions and somehow find a variation in the power used by the tube, the strength of the x-rays generated, or _something_.

Nowadays we have radio telescopes which do more or less what B. was trying to do, but at the time it was just a teen-age boy's wild idea — no more scientifically practical than ten thousand other young amateurs' notions.

B. didn't find what he was looking for; no matter where he aimed his apparatus, no tell-tale differences appeared. But he _did_ find something he _wasn't_ looking for; he found that the x-ray tube generated a _thrust_, as if it wanted to move.

Now, why was it young B. who made this discovery, instead of some scientists of 'standing', or some other user of a Coolidge tube? Well, what scientists of 'standing' would think of experimenting with x-rays as an approach to space-flight? And what user of a

Coolidge tube ever mounted one in delicate balance, so that very small forces would be noticed?

B. was born in 1905; he made his discovery shortly after World War I. He soon learned that the new force was not produced by the x-rays, but by the high voltage which they required. Many experiments were necessary to make certain the force was not one of the <u>known</u> effects of high voltage, and that it is a <u>mass</u> force, like gravity, rather than an <u>area</u> force, like most known electric forces. He finally produced an apparatus which he optimistically called a 'gravitor', a wooden box (four inches square and two feet long) containing some lead and some glass (or sulphur or some other insulating substance), which, when stood upright on a scale and connected to fifty thousand volts, would gain or lose one percent of its weight!

All this was done by a young man just finishing high school. Although there were newspaper reports of his experiments, no scientist of 'standing' expressed any interest. Considering this remarkable fact, young B. decided to proceed very carefully, so he enrolled as a freshman in the nation's finest scientific college and spent his first school year demonstrating to his instructors that he was a first-class 'lab' man.

At the end of this year he sent for his equipment, set it up in his quarters, and sent invitations to those faculty members he felt might have confidence in him — to come and witness 'a demonstration of an electro-gravitational force'.

<u>No one came</u>!

When I first heard this, it seemed so incredible to me that I asked the late Dr Robert Millikan, who had been one of those invited, if anyone had ever found a way of generating or modifying or influencing a gravitational force. "Of course not," he replied, "such a thing is impossible and out of the question!"

It is a sad fact that discoverers are not indestructible. Young Mr. B. was hit very hard by the treatment he received at the hands of his teachers and supposed friends. He ran away and joined the Navy as a 'boot', he has never again, on his own initiative, made any bold

11

attempt to present 'a demonstration of an electro-gravitational force'. Nevertheless, his native scientific ability caused seamen B. to become Lieutenant Commander B. by the middle of World War II. He was placed in charge of the Norfolk radar school, worked too long and too hard, collapsed, and was retired from the Navy in the early nineteen-forties. After six months' rest at home, he came to Lockheed-Vega as an engineer, and that is where I met him.

I found commander B. to be a quiet, modest retiring man — exactly the sort one expects to find in important research installations. He was a brilliant solver of engineering problems, and I soon found that he was more familiar with fundamental physical forces than anyone I have met. So many of us are strictly text-book scientists that it is stimulating to find someone who has first-hand knowledge.

It was many weeks before I learned about Mr. B.'s discovery — and even then it was not from him, but from Jim A., who had himself known B. for quite some time before learning what he told me. I then began questioning B. in detail, because as a mathematician I was interested in trying to discover the field equations involved. B. would not speak in terms of 'gravity' when describing his discovery; he referred to 'stress in dielectrics', which is pertinent but much less sensational. Even so, our understanding of the force-relations, etc., was at this time quite incomplete.

B. and I were separated for some years right after the war, but we kept in touch. When I was teaching calculus to a group of Navy men at Barbers point (which is part of Pearl Harbor), my students built and operated a 'gravitor' and we all became very enthusiastic. The FAWTUFAC Commander took an interest, B. was sent for, and finally no less a personage than CINPAC Admiral Radford witnessed a demonstration. B. was well trusted by his Navy acquaintances, who were of course immensely proud of him, but the demonstrations were still rather primitive, and no scientists appeared. We all thought the millennium was at hand, but it wasn't. Actually, this sort of thing had been going on for years, for even though B. was more of a shrinking violet than a bold promoter, every now and then his friends would try to get _somebody_ interested.

Finally B's friends began to get underway. They rang doorbells all over the country for him — in the academic world, in the business world, and in Washington. B. gave demonstrations by the dozen, but the force was still quite small, and little interest was aroused. Finally, since scientists in America seem to be in the state of the walking dead, it was arranged for B. to go to England and France and continue his search for a conscious scientist. He had a pleasant trip, received some encouragement, and was 'written up' in international air-and-space magazines.

All this time B. was pondering how to increase the force he had discovered. The discovery of a 1% 'lift' should have caused great excitement in the world of science, but it didn't, so how could the 'lift' be increased? Sometime during the Korean War, B. found the answer.

I remember how excited I was on the day I telephoned B. in Washington, after being out of touch for several years, and was told, "the lift isn't just 1% any longer; the apparatus will now lift 110% of its own weight!" My wife and I immediately flew to Washington and with our own eyes saw a moderately heavy gadget made *of metal and Pyrex lift itself right up when 50,000 volts were applied — and float steadily when a slightly lower voltage was used.*

We found that B. and friends have organized a corporation, carried on experiments, applied for over 75 patents in 12 major countries (more than half of which have been granted), and are slowly and patiently giving demonstrations for the Pentagon and key manufacturers in the United States.

It sounds good, doesn't it? Well it isn't. At the present rate of progress, B's company will cause the USA to come to life and start the space age in about 10 to 20 years.

The question is, will the international situation wait that long? Will there be any space age, if we have an atomic war first? You tell me.

Well, damn and blast!! I have never taken much interest in all this excitement about getting into space — in fact, I never cared whether we do or we don't — but if moving out to the planets is going to reduce the possibility of atomic war, why then this space business is damned important! Why doesn't your Mr. B. get in touch with our scientific authorities so that their resources and know-how can be added to his notions?

Sir, he has, and his friends have. Starting with Dr. Einstein himself, virtually every one of our 'leading' scientific authorities has been approached by Mr. B. and/or his friends and this has been going on for some forty years now. It would be difficult for you to name an important scientist was not heard of B.'s discovery, at least at second or third hand.

Well, what's the trouble, then? Surely, once these men have seen B.'s apparatus demonstrated, they would take things in hand and see that things are handled properly. Our best scientific brains can probably make many improvements in B.'s devices.

Yes, sir. That is what young B. thought and what commander B. still thinks. The trouble is, however, that no scientist of 'standing' will attend a demonstration. Many engineers and technical personnel and business people and service men and even some persons of high governmental authority have seen B.'s equipment in operation —- but all scientists of 'repute' find reasons for being elsewhere when a demonstration is given. They just don't show up.

Damnation! Why the hell don't they? Of all the exasperating, stupid, treasonable things I've ever heard of, this is just about the worst! If they don't show up what kind of excuses do they make?

Well, sir, if they can get away with it they do not respond in any way to an invitation. If they have to say something, they try to avoid making any comments about the demonstration and simply explain that they will be out of town at the scheduled time. If the time is changed to suit their convenience, they are 'unavoidably detained'. If they are caught in a corner and pressed for comment they will hold out as long as they can and than explain that they are familiar with Commander B.'s 'findings', that it is simply a known high-voltage phenomenon, a kind of electric 'wind', that it will not work in a vacuum, etc., etc. When one of our most famous scientist, Dr. T., made most of the above remarks, Commander B. Immediately arranged a demonstration of lift in a vacuum of 10^{-6} mm. of Hg (it works better in a vacuum) — but there was no word from Dr. T. He was elsewhere.

Now look here— this kind of behavior is ridiculous, preposterous and absurd. Certainly every responsible scientist should investigate any reasonable proposition that is put to him — that's part of his job. We look to our scientist for guidance; they are supposed to tell us what is possible and what is impossible, what is practical and what is a waste of time — and, damn it all, they are supposed to be upright and honorable people, not devious and crooked and sneaky. What the hell is the matter with them?

Sir, it took me some time to find the answer to that question, because I'm a scientist myself, and it was difficult for me to get the proper perspective. What is wrong with our scientists is that they (and the rest of us, too) have a lot of silly ideas about science and scientists. We are told that the study of science is 'ennobling', and that it produces people who are a cut above the rest of us, more dedicated, less worldly, more honest, less corrupt – and so on. This, of course, is just so much malarkey; one does not become wise or virtuous by studying physics or chemistry or mathematics. There are rare individuals who become creative scientists by means of much self-questioning, and this same self-questioning is a source of wisdom and virtue – but, unfortunately, self-

questioning is not encouraged or taught in our scientific schools.

What happens when almost everyone thinks that scientists, as a class, are wise and good while the rest of us, comparatively speaking, are foolish and evil? I can illustrate this best by telling about a conversation I had some time ago with my friend T., a scientist. T. was saying that he didn't believe a scientist should be head of a business— never more than Director of Research. I asked him if he thought it was proper for a scientist to earn $15,000 per year. "Yes," he said, "some scientists earn that."

"How about $20,000 per year?" I asked him.

"Yes, I think that would be all right."

"What about $50,000?" I wanted to know.

"Oh, no! That would be too much," he protested.

"Then perhaps you should wear your collar backward, T." I grinned at him.

He smiled and said, "Yes, it _is_ something like that."

Now, sir, I believe that T. protested against $50,000 per year because he believed that a man making that much money could not retain the impartiality which the scientist must have. I know many scientists and scholars who like to think of themselves as living inconspicuously in a quiet, comfortable home — detached and aloof from the world of everyday living. They think of the rest of us as greedy folk who want much more than this. Most of them do not think they think and feel this way, but they do.

You, sir, are experienced in the ways of the world, and know something of life. Isn't it a fact that quiet, comfortable homes are more expensive than noisy, uncomfortable ones? Isn't it true that scientists eat and drink and breed pretty much as other people do, and that scientists' families have the same need of food, shelter, and clothing as do non-scientists' families?

So here we have a class of people who think they want less, while actually they want more, who limit their earnings without limiting their desires, and who think they are wiser and better than the common herd when, in fact, they are not only no better than others but also too stupid to know it!

What can be expected of such people?

It can be expected that they will live in _fear_.

Fear of what? Fear of anything that might threaten their already insufficient income, and since the scientists' income and security are dependent upon his prestige or 'standing' or reputation, scientists in general live in fear of anything which threatens prestige, 'standing', or reputation.

And what is it that can ruin a scientist's status more effectively than anything else? Just being identified with some program or project or doctrine or gadget that at some later time is 'discredited' or laughed at or simply regarded as 'old-fashioned' or 'out-of-date'.

This is a chance that no 'reputable' scientist will take; if there is a possibility that some particular scientific event may turn out to be *a fiasco, no 'reputable' scientist will go anywhere near it. In our personal preoccupation with Mr. B.'s approach to space as a means to world peace, we have been asking scientists to risk their entire livelihood by witnessing a demonstration; it is not fair to expect them to do this. It is tragic, but, so far as anything really <u>new</u> is concerned, all our scientists are <u>dead</u>.*

H'm. You tell a sad story, I must admit. I'm not sure that I accept it, but, for the time being, I'll concede that no help can be expected from our scientists. Damn, that's a nasty thought! But you said other people had come to B.'s demonstrations. What about the business men? Surely <u>they</u> must have been excited about the possibilities!

Yes, sir, they were — at least for a while. But it seems that the sickness which has incapacitated our scientists has affected us all. No business man will make a move in the world of science without first getting the approval of a scientist of 'standing'. The presidents of hundred-million-dollar corporations have been enthusiastic about B.'s discovery — until they have asked their own staff scientists for an opinion. What can a frightened man say when such a question is put to him?

If he says, "Yes, B.'s discovery is sound" his company may find out quickly that he is mistaken, and he will forever after be known as the supposed 'scientist' who endorsed B.'s gadget! If he says, "No, B.'s discovery is nothing new," his statement may never be disproven, but, even if it is, he will probably lose his job, but not his status as a scientist. In the scientific world you can obstruct progress as long as you like, without losing 'face', but you take your life in your hands when you try to help progress along, even when you are right.

Commander B. has a son in college, majoring in physical culture. His father had hoped he would take up some kind of scientific career, but the young B. said, "Dad, I wouldn't go through what you've gone through for anything in the world!"

Stop it, I say! There is no need to get maudlin about it! The situation is bad, I admit, but you talk as if it were the end of the world.

Well, sir —

Yes, yes, I'll say it for you — perhaps it is the end of the world, at least for us. If we have really got to the point where new knowledge is outlawed, and nothing can be done about it, then this civilization is on its last legs. But dammit, man! I don't like to give up without a fight. Maybe something can be done. If our scientists can be made to see what they've done to themselves or maybe our business people can be told what is wrong with the scientists, or something! Can't you think of something?

Yes, sir, I think about this quite a lot. It isn't easy to live with a situation of this kind, without trying to do something about it. I've tried all kinds of things, some of which seem to be working slowly, like B.'s corporation. Just lately I decided to try something really wild, something no one in his right mind would ever dream of doing — under normal circumstances, that is. But present circumstances aren't normal, and neither is this scheme of mine. I am writing a book with the express purpose of proving to people how stupid they are — certainly a stupid undertaking if I ever heard of one! Of course the real stupids won't read it, because they'll be sure it isn't meant for them. But there are a few people left in the world who are more-or-less conscious (how they have survived I don't know), and I would like to reach them, if I can.

If a few hundred or a few thousand really _conscious_ people can be 'alerted' to this impossible situation, perhaps something constructive can be done.

No one likes to be called 'stupid', but if a person can be made to see his own stupidity, then that stupidity disappears. This, at least, is my experience. I have made some discoveries myself, in mathematics, electronics, psychotherapy and plain everyday living, and each discovery has arrived at the same time as a realization of my own stupidity. In fact, I think that the two experiences are identical; to realize that something is stupid is to discover how to get along without it.

Can this be the secret of true education? Do we become wise only by becoming aware of our foolishness? If so, it is no wonder that we are so foolish and stupid, for it is our habit to tell ourselves and the world how wonderful we are, and we hide from our faults. As citizens of the world we are stupid, because we are too lazy to think for ourselves, and because we allow our thinking to be done for us by 'experts' who are more dishonest than we are. If we realize this we will graduate from it. In our fear, we have sought guidance from those who are more frightened than we are; if we see this we will stop it. In our foolishness, we have relied upon the integrity of those who deceive themselves even more than we do — surely there are less messy ways to commit suicide!

Do you really think that calling people 'stupid' is going to open their eyes?

No — atomic bombs may break their bones, but names will never touch them. I don't think it is of any use to _tell_ people they are stupid; they must see it for themselves before anything is accomplished. They will be annoyed and angry at _me_ if I merely call them names, even if I am correct in what I call them; they will be annoyed and angry at themselves if I somehow enable them to _see_ their own stupidities.

In my home we have a family saying that is somewhat to the point. When one of us does something which indicates extraordinary unconsciousness, that one is awarded the 'stupid' prize for the day. Whoever witnesses the idiotic achievement will say, "I hereby award you the 'stupid' prize for today," or words to that effect. Having won this prize myself times without number, I feel qualified to present it to others.

There is a saying, "Eternal vigilance is the price of liberty." 'Vigilance' means watching, looking, inquiring, investigating — being conscious of what is happening. We have lost our liberty because we weren't looking; we were asleep.

To all of us who are inclined to think or feel that it is safe to live without looking into and investigating what happens in us and around us, I hereby award the 'stupid' prize.

To every person (whether scientist or non-scientist) who has the idea that scientists should not be too wealthy because it will make them less inclined to tell the truth — the 'stupid' prize.

To each person who thinks it is easy for a scientist to endorse a really new thing — one 'stupid' prize.

To each businessman or government official who thinks that a supposed scientific discovery or invention is 'without merit' because some scientist of 'standing' has said so, or because no such scientist has, as yet, approved of it — one gold-plated, carefully engraved 'stupid' prize.

A special message to each of these prize-winners is on the cover of this book.

The original book cover

THE COUNTRY OF THE BLIND

The hard-core of science is mathematics. When the laws of a science can be expressed in quantitative mathematical formulae, it is considered that something is known about that particular science. Even in fields of science which consist largely of not-yet-understood observational data, there is a mathematical science called 'statistics' which is used to evaluate the data. Behind the doctor, the psychologist, the sociologist, the chemist and the physicist stands the mathematician — the man who makes the rules.

But what if the mathematician is stupid? If the man who makes the rules think that 2+2 = 5, what price science?

Do you have faith in science? Do you believe that the scientists and their rule-makers the mathematicians know what they are doing? If you do, get ready for a shock, for I propose to show that our orthodox mathematicians believe (or profess to believe) that there are just as many even numbers as there are numbers (odd and even), and other stupidities (which even include 2+2 = 5)!

Now, don't bury your head in the sand just because we're going to talk about mathematics — if you can count while sitting on your hands, you will be able to understand what is going on. For we are going to tackle mathematicians where they are stupid, not where they are smart, and stupidity is not very complicated.

There is a famous book called "Tristram Shandy" in which a man of that name tries to tell the story of his life. The difficulty is that, after four years of writing, he finds he is only told about the first four days of his life! Being a sensible fellow, he concludes that, at that rate, he will never complete his autobiography.

Nevertheless in many orthodox mathematical texts such as are used in our own colleges and universities, it is explained that, if Tristram Shandy were to live forever, he would inevitably complete writing his life story. Why? Because, no matter what day of his life we consider, there will come a year in which the account of that day will be written. The one-billion-and-ninth day, for example? It will be described during the one-billion-and-ninth year of Shandy's life. Thus the matter is 'proven'.

What you will not find in the text-books or hear expounded in the class-rooms is reasoning such as the following:

Shandy wrote for 4 times 365 days and covered four days of his life; he thus wrote about 1/365th of the time he spent writing. If he lived forever and wrote at the same rate, he would still complete only 1/365th of his life story. Thus in 365,000 days of writing he would describe 2000 days of living, in 365 trillion days of writing he would describe one trillion days of living, and so on. No matter how great the time spent writing only 1/365th of that period will be described. He will never complete more than 1/365th part of his autobiography; not even living forever would enable him to finish 2/365ths of it.

Even Shandy himself could see this, but our orthodox mathematicians can't. They say that by living forever he will finish it all.

If all that were at stake with the literary difficulties of the fictitious Tristram Shandy, I wouldn't trouble you about this, but _this is a sample of the thinking of our supposedly best brains_!!

How did it all start?

Well, it didn't start with Galileo. In one of his writings he says that we can take any number and name its double or its square, so it kind of looks like there are just as many squares or even numbers as there are numbers, but hold on! This doesn't make sense, so whoa up, here! Let's leave this alone. Galileo knew enough to come in out of the rain.

Perhaps the trouble began with Bernard Bolzano, who died more than a hundred years ago, and who was in some respects a fairly sensible man. He said that, when we talk about infinite things like an endless string of numbers (such as 1,2,3 and so on forever), we get into difficulties and contradictions and paradoxes, and he tried to clear up the difficulties and warn against the contradictions. But due to a curious habit that intellectuals have, the work of Bolzano did more harm than good, because (a) it gave everyone the impression that the art of reasoning about giant numbers had been well worked-out (since Bolzano did clear up a number of foggy points) and (b) since the rest of his work was so good, everybody accepted his mistakes as truth.

This unfortunate affliction of intellectuals is the habit of borrowing or copying what someone else said without bothering to investigate whether or not it is correct. In the history of almost any science you will find that all but about one out of eight or ten 'authorities' copied what other 'authorities' had written, including their errors, while the few real authorities were actually interested in the subject they wrote about and did some experimenting and sometimes learned something. Unfortunately, there is such a thing as being too interested, being so eager to find out something that we can persuade ourselves (and others, too) that we have found out something, when we have only 'found out' something which isn't so.

Georg Cantor was such a mistaken 'authority', a kind and gentle man who flourished in the 1870s and 'found out' many things which are not so. Cantor wrote so impressively and persuasively that the majority of orthodox mathematicians have 'bought' his ideas and regard them as a vital part of mathematical knowledge. Along with Richard Dedekind and others, Cantor produced much of the mathematical theology which is replacing mathematics.

Let me quote one of our leading contemporary 'authorities':

"The actual creator of the general theory of sets as an independent mathematical discipline was the great German mathematician G. Cantor (1845-1918); we are indebted to him, in particular, for the analysis of such concepts as equality in power, cardinal number, infinity and order - Cantor set theory is one of those mathematical disciplines which are in a state of especially intensive development. Its ideas and lines of thought have penetrated into almost all branches of mathematics and have exerted everywhere most stimulating and fertilizing influence."

Fertilizer, indeed.

Cantor started out by taking common sense and splitting it in two. Suppose you are a child and cannot count. In front of you are two piles of fruit, a pile of oranges and a pile of apples.

How can you find out whether or not the numbers of oranges is the same as the number of apples? Just pick up an orange in one hand and an apple in the other and put the pair somewhere else; keep on repeating this until you can't do it any more. If no oranges or apples are left over, there are just as many oranges as there are apples. If there are oranges left over, there are more oranges; if there are apples left over, there are more apples. This is a simple, common-sense procedure which Tristram Shandy would approve.

The mathematicians call it 'the method of one-to-one correspondence' and they use it to 'prove' more nonsense than you can shake a stick at. In doing so they follow Cantor, who taught them how.

The sensible use of 1-to-1 correspondence calls for two rules:

1. Two bunches of things may be compared by putting them together in twos, on a 1-to-1 basis. This rule is accepted by Cantor and the other orthodox mathematicians.

2. The 1-to-1 pairing of things must be carried out from the beginning to end before any conclusions can be drawn. If we put the

child down by a pile of oranges and a pile of apples, see that the child starts pairing the oranges and apples on a 1-to-1 basis, and we then walk out of the room before the work is finished, we are in no position to say whether the two kinds of fruit are equal or unequal in number. This rule is ignored by Cantor and the other orthodox mathematicians.

The two rules make good sense, don't they? All we have to do is eliminate the second rule, get on our horse and gallop off in all directions, and we have Cantor's mathematics.

Cantor: There are just as many even numbers as there are numbers.
'Proof': arrange the numbers 1, 2, 3, etc. in one line and their doubles in another line, thus:

numbers	1	2	3	4	5	6	7	8	9	10	11	12	13	14
	|	|	|	|	|	|	|	|	|	|	|	|	|	|
doubles	2	4	6	8	10	12	14	16	18	20	22	24	26	28

Thus we see (or do we?) That all whole numbers and all even numbers can be brought into a 1-to-1 correspondence. Therefore there are just as many even numbers as there are whole numbers.

Kitselman (and Shandy, too I think): between 1 and 100 inclusive there are 50 even numbers; thus half of the first hundred whole numbers are even numbers. Half of the first million whole numbers are even numbers. Half of the first trillion whole numbers are even numbers. Increasing the number of whole numbers does not affect the ratio; half of all whole numbers are even numbers. Half of all numbers end in 0, 2, 4, 6, or 8; these are the 'even' numbers. Half of all numbers can be divided by two; these are the even numbers. There are more arguments, but why whip a dead horse?

Cantor: there are just as many squares as there are numbers.
'Proof: arrange the numbers and their squares into lines, thus:

numbers	1	2	3	4	5	6	7
squares	1	4	9	16	25	36	49

Obviously (!), There is a 1-2-1 correspondence, so there are just as many squares as there are numbers.

Kitselman & Shandy: in the first 10 whole numbers, there are 3 square numbers. In the first hundred numbers, there are 10 square numbers. In the first 1000 numbers, there are 31 square numbers. In the first million numbers, there are 1000 squares. In the first trillion numbers, there are 1 million squares. In general, there are n squares in the first n^2 numbers, so that there are many more whole numbers than square numbers.

Cantor: there are just as many fractions as there are numbers

'Proof: arrange numbers and fractions in two lines, thus:

numbers	1	2	3	4	5	6	7	8	9	10	11	12	13	14
fractions	$\frac{1}{1}$	$\frac{2}{1}$	$\frac{1}{2}$	$\frac{3}{1}$	$\frac{1}{3}$	$\frac{3}{2}$	$\frac{2}{3}$	$\frac{4}{1}$	$\frac{1}{4}$	$\frac{4}{2}$	$\frac{2}{4}$	$\frac{4}{3}$	$\frac{3}{4}$	$\frac{5}{1}$

(Publishers note: It has been a challenge to get the fractions as Kitselman wrote them in this book correct due to his unique writing style. It appears to be Cantor's so called diagonal method or diagonal argument sequence.)

Since fractions can be arranged in a 1-to-1 pairing with the whole numbers, they are equally numerous.

Kitselman - Shandy: with the first 10 numbers we can construct 100 fractions. With the first thousand numbers we can write a million fractions. With the first million numbers we can write a trillion fractions. In general, with the first n numbers we can make n^2 fractions, so that there are vastly more fractions than whole numbers.

I am sorry to say that many of the supposedly basic ideas about numbers, which are today considered to be fundamental in mathematics, are based upon the notions of Cantor. Perhaps you have heard that 'an infinite collection of things is a part of itself'. This follows from Cantor's 'proof' that there are as many even numbers as whole numbers, for the infinity of whole numbers contained the infinity of even numbers, which Cantor says is equally numerous!

Bolzano, Dedekind and Cantor also propagated a lot of nonsense about the number of points on a line, or in a plane, etc. Since points are defined as having no dimensions, there are, of course, no way of considering how many points are in a line, etc. Modern mathematics is riddled with these ridiculous notions.

To be perfectly fair, Georg Cantor is to be regarded as our principal mistaken 'authority' only because our orthodox mathematicians think so highly of him. It was Richard

Dedekind who 'established' that an infinite bunch of things is a part of itself; in fact he defined an infinite set or class or bunch as one which is equal to part of itself. Bolzano knew better, but he was dead and gone when Cantor came into contact with Dedekind's ideas, also Bolzano was not widely read at that time. So without Bolzano to warn him and protect him, it may be that Cantor was led down the garden path by Dedekind.

Most of our contemporary mathematicians do not see anything wrong with the following: "A set may happen to be an element of itself. For example, someone (the name has escaped us) has suggested that the set of all abstract ideas; such a set is certainly an element of itself if we grant (and who wouldn't!) that it is itself an abstract idea." All of this, including the parenthetical remarks is quoted from a leading textbook on the foundations of mathematics. It is the kind of statement that we can read easily enough without detecting any serious flaw — if we are merely intellectual, that is.

But anyone who has learned how to be observant is likely to ponder more-or-less as follows: "What is an 'abstract idea'? Well an 'idea' is something which I can look at with my 'mind', be it a pictureable thing or a word or the concept of a triangle or the notion of femininity or what-not. An 'abstract' idea is an idea which is not picturable or audible or tangible or smellable or tasteable. Now, what is the 'set' of all abstract ideas? The _name_ 'the set of all abstract ideas' is, of course, an idea, and an abstract one at that — but what is it that is being _named_? Obviously, it is all the abstract ideas there are, all taken together. Can I look at all abstract ideas with my mind? Certainly not all at once, nor even one at a time (since there is not time enough); also, there are, doubtless, abstract ideas which _I_ am not able to perceive with _my_ mind, but which nevertheless _can_ be perceived by the minds of others. Can I see them collectively, as one sees a forest without seeing a single tree? No, for I do not say that I can 'see' a forest unless I can see its shape, and I cannot see the 'shape' of all-abstract-ideas-taken-together. So 'the set of all abstract ideas' is _not_ an abstract idea is therefore _not_ a part of itself. I cannot agree with the statement as quoted."

No one has ever shown me a four-sided triangle, and I don't think anyone ever will. It may be that someone, someday will show me something which is a part of itself, but I doubt it.

Perhaps you are wondering why our mathematicians swallow all this nonsense. There are several reasons. First of all, many mathematicians become so addicted to the use of symbols that they _think_ in terms of symbols instead of the numbers they represent. Numbers are not symbols; symbols are the _names_ of numbers, and many crazy things can be done with the names of numbers, which cannot be done with _numbers_. Dedekind and Cantor forgot this, and thousands have followed their example.

Secondly, since many mathematical processes consist of a series of logical steps, multitudes of mathematicians are not only symbol-happy but logic-happy. These unfortunate souls seem to have forgotten that mathematics has to do with numbers, which is about like forgetting the breathing has to do with air. I sometimes feel that, just as in other professions, many people become mathematicians who do not _like_ mathematics, and who consequently try to escape from numbers into other fields (while still drawing pay as mathematicians, that is).

One of the best illustrations of this latter trait (hang your clothes on a hickory limb, but don't go near the water) is Cantor's celebrated 'proof' that, between any 2 numbers, there are more than an infinity of 'real' numbers. This one seems to have been swallowed hook, line, rod and reel by more than half of our mathematicians, and yet I cannot see how anyone could accept it unless it is agreed in advance that one will never look at it closely, think about it, or test it.

Consider the numbers 1, 2, 3, 4, 5 and so on; Cantor says there are N of them, N here being a kind of 'standard' infinity. Suppose we put a decimal point in front of each of these, thus : .1, .2, .3, .4, .5, etc. if these numbers go on forever, they will list every possible number between 0.1 (one-tenth) and one, won't they? Well Cantor said that if we imagine all the numbers listed in this way, he will show us how to construct a number that is different from any number in our list, thus proving that N numbers aren't enough to fill the space between 0.1 and 1.0 Such a proof would be as astounding as mathematicians say it is, if it only were worth the powder to blow it up!

How does Cantor construct his 'unincluded' number? Well, imagine _all_ the numbers between one-tenth and one, all written down on an infinite piece of paper. The first digit of Cantor's number is _anything_ but the first digit of our first number. The second digit of Cantor's number is _anything_ but the second digit of our second number. And so on — the nth digit of Cantor's number is _anything_ but the nth digit of our nth number.

Thus Cantor's number is different from each of our numbers (no matter how many there are) in at least one decimal place, and the 'proof is complete. Damnably clever, isn't it?

Damnably.

Kitselman is tired of contending against Cantor, let Shandy do it.

Shandy: all one-digit numbers between 1/10 and 1 are included in our list; it is not possible to construct any other one-digit number between 1/10 and 1. All two-digit numbers between 1/10 and 1 are included; it is not possible to construct another. All N-digit numbers between 1/10 and 1 are included; it is not possible to construct another. Increasing the number of digits does not change this state of affairs; Cantor's 'different' number is a rabbit with horns.

It is as if the Cantorians have no inclination towards mathematics, so they cut out paper dolls instead. This is all right with me, as long as it isn't called 'mathematics'. Henri Poincare (1854-1912), who was perhaps the last great mathematician we have had, enthusiastically welcomed the first news about Cantor's attack upon the infinite, but before long he stated emphatically that 'most of the concepts and conclusions of the Cantor theory of sets should be excluded from mathematics'.

This leads directly to the third reason why there is so much stupidity in our mathematics. The great Poincare spoke out in condemnation, not only of Cantorian notions, but of addiction to 'logic' as well — yet the Cantorians and the logicians are now in the majority. I know many able mathematicians who do not 'buy' the orthodox articles of faith in modern mathematics, yet they see no reason to speak out in church; if even Poincaré's protest was ineffective, what could theirs accomplish? Mathematics (and science in general, for that matter) is a great organism which badly needs to go to the bathroom.

To learn a fourth reason for our mathematical stupidity, consider the question, "if you are employed to teach mathematics, a subject you neither like nor understand, but nevertheless you want to hold on to your job — how do you keep your students from discovering your incompetence?" You use brain-crushers. In various ways you assert that black is white, 'prove' it authoritatively with big words, backup your 'proof' with mistaken 'authorities' like Georg Cantor, ram the students objections down their throats and convince them that their reasoning powers are defective. You ruin a few good intellects in doing this, of course, but your precious job is safe. And besides, you have taught your students one of the basic principles of modern living — that you can't beat City Hall.

Tommy is a young friend of mine who attends high school in a town near my home. He is a class president, an athlete, and an honor student who takes the advanced courses which are being made available for the few remaining high school students who want to learn something. I asked Tommy to read these pages and tell me his reactions.

Tommy reacted as most people do when they hear both sides of the Cantorian argument. I told him that many people simply do not believe that orthodox mathematicians teach such absurdities, and offered to show him textbook examples. "You don't have too," he said. "I am taking a course in Advanced Mathematics, and just a week or so ago we talked about infinite sets." I asked him what happened. "Our teacher tried to convince us that there are just as many even numbers as there are numbers," said Tommy, "but we didn't convince. He tried to prove it to us, but didn't succeed, so he said that it is just a _fact_ which we would have to accept if we were going to get onto the next subject. So we 'accepted' it — most of us with reservations, of course." I asked how the students felt about this. "We are disappointed," Tommy replied, "because we thought mathematics was one subject in which teacher and students reason together to find out what is true. Now it seems that we must accept some things on an 'or else' basis, and if this is what mathematics is — well, who wants it?"

At this point my wife Betsy spoke up and reminded Tommy that children frequently have to pretend that they know less than their teachers, just as Tommy and his classmates have pretended that they accept Cantor's twaddle. "As long as you know that you are pretending, Tommy," she added, "you'll be all right."

I think this is true, but the trouble is — suppose Tommy or one of his classmates decides to play the part of the conscious hypocrite in order to go on studying mathematics and eventually get a degree; this will take nine years, and by the end of that time he is very likely to forget that he is pretending! I think this is how most of our orthodox mathematicians got to be the way they are.

It will not startle you very much to learn that a fifth reason for the stupidity of our orthodox mathematicians is that most of them _are_ stupid — not necessarily much more stupid than the rest of us, but certainly not less stupid. Like the rest of us, they think that it is all right to be careless and dishonest about the work we do, that it is all right to maintain our position by taking advantage of others, that it is good enough to just 'get by'.

Would you like to find an honest mathematician? There are some, and I will give you 3 questions with which you can identify them:

    1.   What is halfway between adding and multiplying? Most mathematicians will ask you what you mean by this question, or by 'half way', or what are you getting at — but don't you give an inch! Say, "I don't know what I mean: that is why I'm asking. I understand that mathematicians have investigated just about everything, and I've heard that adding and multiplying are perhaps the two most basic processes in all mathematics — so I am asking you, sir, to tell me what is halfway between these two simple processes. Taking two numbers like 3 and 5, if I add them I get 8, and if I multiply them I get 15; but if I do something to them which is neither adding nor multiplying but somehow midway between the 2, I may get 11.3 or some

such number. What is the operation which is midway between adding and multiplying? If you don't know, sir, how would you go about finding out? As to what I am getting at, I want to find out whether mathematics has answers to simple questions like this one, or is it a science which is not yet very well organized and understood."

2.   What number is its own natural logarithm? Again, you will be asked counter-questions, but stick your ground! Say, "I understand that the exponential function, and its inverse, the logarithm, are considered to be the two most basic functions in all calculus. So I assume Sir, that if anything much is known about higher mathematics, these two functions must be known backwards, forwards, up-and-down, and sideways. Therefore I ask for the root (or roots) of these functions, this being, in my opinion, one of the simplest and most basic questions I could ask about higher mathematics. What number, sir, is equal to its own logarithm - and, therefore, equal to its own exponential? I understand that higher mathematics solves all kinds of equations; please, sir, solve these two little basic ones for me.

$$X = E^X \qquad x = \log x$$

Can you give me a formula for the answer? My friend Kitselman says the basic root is a complex number, approximately one-third plus four-thirds i, which he has calculated to 18 decimals and calls by the Russian letter 'zheh', Ж, which he considers 'real fancy'. He says Ж is as important as Е or π (symbol)."

3.   Is the following proof of valid?

Given : All the men who have ever lived, are living now or may live in the future.

To prove : each man has one eye.

Proof : stand the men in a line facing us and extending to the right. Number the men (perhaps by painting 1, 2, 3, 4, etc. on their foreheads) and number the eyes (perhaps by painting 1, 2, 3, 4, etc. on the eyelids). These 2 series of numbers can be placed in a 1-to-1 correspondence; for every man there is this corresponding eye. The 37th man may be paired with the 37th eye, the millionth man with the millionth eye, and so on. You cannot name a man (by number, that is) for whom there is not a corresponding eye — nor can you name an eye for which there is not a corresponding man. The 1-to-1 correspondence is complete, and the number of men is thus shown to be equal to the number of eyes. This being so each man has one eye.

Don't tell this to the mathematician unless he rejects the above 'proof', but since "in the country of the blind, the one-eyed man is king", this proof makes every man a king. The country of the blind, of course, is where mistaken 'authorities' rule.

What will you find when you ask mathematicians these three questions? First of all, defense reactions — because, even if you are as humble as Socrates talking with Euthyphro, these questions are a challenge to Established Authority in general and to its underpaid priests in particular. You will be asked to define your terms, state clearly what you mean, etc., so that you will have to stick out your chin and become the defender instead of the attacker. Since you cannot state your question clearly, how can it be answered? And so on. At this point you must somehow convince the poor frightened man that you are not a threat of any kind, that you just want information. If you succeed in doing this (which isn't likely), or if your man really likes mathematics and therefore feels secure and adequately compensated in his pursuit of it, you will hear words which come easily only from the lips of wise and honest persons, such as, "I don't know" and "I have often wondered about that".

Mathematicians will tell you that question #1 has many possible answers; ask them which answer, in their opinion, would be most basic. Question #2 has a definite answer and you will find a few rare men who know something about it, or how to go about finding out. Question #3 is, of course, a test for Cantorians; to them, it is a perfectly valid proof. (Oh, they may object to the last sentence in the 'proof', but they <u>will</u> accept the sentence before that.)

Please remember that you are not out to persecute professional mathematicians — only to learn whether or not they are as stupid as the rest of us. It is <u>our</u> own stupidity that we are trying to discover, so that we may graduate from it, and this stupidity consists in putting our faith in people who are as stupid as we are. It is not for us to denounce the mathematician as a hypocrite and a charlatan when his only real crime is that he is as irresponsible as we are. It is important for us to see that our idols have feet of clay — just like ours, in fact — but the pot does not call the kettle 'black' with any attitude of superiority. So be kind to the mathematicians when you make them uncomfortable; they are people, too.

Some people who have read these words feel that after all, mathematics is a theoretical subject and that even if _all_ our mathematicians were a bit dotty, it wouldn't hurt 'Science' as a whole. They suggest that Kitselman exaggerates the importance of Cantorian eccentricities, etc. because he is himself a mathematician and happens to be 'steamed up' on the subject.

The charge that I am 'steamed up' is quite true; I am ornery, arrogant, dissatisfied and disrespectful, and my fellow mathematicians are likely to think of me as mean, nasty and hateful, too. But I do not exaggerate, at least not very much.

Physicists often consider 'fields' of various kinds of forces which stretch out to infinity. Not being mathematicians, they do not know that Poincare and others have criticized Cantor's notions about infinity, so they have swallowed Cantor's mumbo-jumbo without even a _grain_ of salt. Accordingly, their notions about infinite force-fields are as cockeyed as can be

— and they don't even know it! This is one reason why, when somebody discovers some new kind of force or use of forces, our big scientists reject the discovery without investigation.

Perhaps it contradicts Cantor!

Entirely apart from my fulminations against the Cantorians, the symbolists and the logicians, many people are astonished that mathematicians know so little about questions 1 and 2, which have nothing to do with these controversial subjects.

There is a reason for this, and it governs all science. If it hasn't been enunciated before, it can be known as Kitselman's law:
"We are more likely to report our accomplishments than our frustrations."

The numbers E or π are found in text-books because there are formulae for them and they can be calculated easily; the number $Ж$ is not found in text-books because no one has found a formula for it and it is not easy to calculate. Yet I do not doubt that mathematical explorers have repeatedly tackled all three numbers, since they are nearly equal in importance.

After all, who is going to write a paper saying, "Here is a number which I have found but can't find a formula for, etc."?

What is easy, we announce; what is hard, we sweep under the rug. We brag about our hits and forget about our misses; this is how we become stupid.

THE VOLCANO

Kitselman, you sound to me like a sorehead. I have read your remarks about Mr. B. and the orthodox mathematicians, and I don't like your attitude! Who do you think you are — Jesus? You talk about learned and respected men in just about the same way that Jesus talked about the scribes and the Pharisees! It makes me hot under the collar, I tell you, and when I investigate (as I have) and find out that the charges you have made are *true*, my blood is beginning to boil! You have no right to be so *right* when you attack people and institutions I respect.

Or did, that is. I don't claim to be very rational about this, but I am annoyed at the way you talk about Cantor, even though I agree with you and Shandy in every point. You just rub me the wrong way, I guess, so much so that I find myself wanting to defend Bolzano, Dedekind and Cantor — simply because you attack them — and wanting to argue with Poincare — simply because he is on your side.

In that case, sir, perhaps it would be best for you to forget about Commander B. and Kitselman's onslaughts against respectable mathematicians. For, as you say, who is

Kitselman? Bolzano and Dedekind and Cantor were good and kind men who have been honored and respected by good and kind men for many years now. They are dead and gone; let them rest in peace. Poincare too, was a good and kind man, far too gentlemanly to be classed with Kitselman the sorehead. Let all these matters rest, sir, and go your way in peace.

Frankly, I wish I could, but it's not that easy, as you know very well, you rascal! You have succeeded in making me very uncomfortable, and it isn't just the way you talk — it's the facts that you point to. I don't know, for example, whether your Commander B. is fictitious or real, or whether his 'discovery' exists — but I do know that our leading scientists do act in the ways you have described whenever they are approached about something really new. I know this because I have acquaintances who have made discoveries, which may or may not be of value, and who are unable to get a hearing from scientists of 'standing', as you call them. I have acquaintances who are scientists of 'standing', and I have seen them behave like mediaeval churchmen when faced with a challenge to their beliefs. I'm sorry to say that I have respected and admired these obstructors of progress, these pompous, conceited…

Steady, now. Was their mistake so much greater than yours, sir? You respected and admired them, you say — isn't that exactly what <u>they</u> did? If I am so respected and admired by others that I begin to respect and admire myself, how can I possibly be expected to see the virtues of something foreign to my beliefs? If you yourself have helped to persuade the scientist that he stands on a pedestal, how can you object because the poor man believes you?

Say no more; I am beginning to think this way myself. I hereby award myself the 'stupid' prize, because I've been too lazy to think clearly, and because I have put all important thinking into hands as irresponsible as my own. I have been so careless and indolent that many supposedly learned persons have been accepted by me as 'authorities' largely because they speak and write in big and obscure words — yet now in a sudden flash I see that writing and talking obscurely is the refuge and disguise of incompetence. I am ashamed — because I have accepted all these people at their face value, because I have almost never looked at them critically, and because, in almost all the important things, I have 'let George do it', without even realizing (though often suspecting) that 'George' is an ass!

(Publishers note: the phrase 'let George do it' was popularised in the 1940s by Kitselman's friend Max Freedom Long in his books on Huna to mean the action of the unconscious or sub-conscious mind.)

Sir, this is a depressing realization. But, after all, it is 'George' the scientist, 'George' the industrialist, and 'George' the government official who are really to blame, isn't it? Your sin is merely that you trusted not wisely but too well, wouldn't you say? Even if it is true that our 'authorities' have been rendered conceited (and therefore foolish) by the praise of others, you yourself have contributed only a small part of that praise. So if you are guilty in this manner, surely it is only an infinitesimal guilt, sir; you need not take on so. I'm sure you have many fine qualities, and have tried to lead a good life to the best of your ability; what more can anyone expect of any man?

Infinitesimal, my eye! If we have a world disaster, my death will only be an infinitesimal part of the general dying, no doubt — but not to me, friend, not to me! If my infinitesimal part of the world's guilt leads up to my infinitesimal part of the world's death, then I am <u>guilty</u> <u>unto</u> <u>death</u>, and this is not, to me an infinitesimal matter — — Bolzano, Dedekind, Cantor, Kitselman, Shandy and Poincare to the contrary notwithstanding! I don't want you to minimize my guilt and let 'George' be the guilty one; I have been blaming everyone else for the world's troubles for so long that it actually feels good to be guilty. For if I am guilty, I am responsible, I count for something, I have some value in the world. For years I have had the idea that the world goes its way regardless of me, and that I am not in any way responsible for the condition of the world. Now I see that this is not true. I am one of those who make the world the way it is, one of those who make — or break — the world. Up until now I've been like a sleep-walker, but now I think I am beginning to wake up.

Please, sir, not so fast! Do not wake up too quickly, for you may not be where you think you are. Responsibility is exciting, I know, but it is very real and very deep. From this point on, please be as careful as you would be in a bullring or on a battlefield. I do not say this because your life is in danger — since all our lives are in danger — but because your 'peace of mind' is threatened. To feel somewhat responsible, as you do, for the errors of our scientists, financiers, and government men, is stimulating and invigorating, but it will not upset you too much. You will 'put not your trust in fools', you can look down upon those who do, and your self-esteem will be relatively undisturbed. At least you have accepted that

What the world is is the result of what we did with what it was; we are getting exactly what we deserve.

If you realize this fully, you will have nothing to complain about, and to the end of your days you will enjoy peace of mind. Be content with this, sir, and go no further. Except my thanks for your kind attention, live quietly, enjoy good health, and read no more of these pages.

Persons who read this page are entitled to know why the rest of the book is sealed. It is because

What the world will be is the result of what we do with what is; we will get exactly what we deserve.

The rest of these pages are about what we can do to make a better world. If the first part of this book has affected you very much, this last part may stimulate you into action, so please consider carefully before you break the seal.

Most of us read for entertainment or relaxation or to get information; we do not expect our reading to interfere with our everyday living. Our daily activities take up our time, and we do not want to be compelled to engage in new activities.

The pages which follow contain information which _may_ _compel_ you to engage in certain activities which will interfere with your present plans. It is not I who will persuade you; you will persuade yourself with your own perception of certain facts.

So if for any reason you don't want to be swept into the stream, stop here! This book is yours; break the seal if you like. But don't complain to me later — I warned you!

You say that responsibility is very real and very deep. Please tell me more about this.

Very well. Suppose some tyrant is planning to put some blameless man to death, but, after being appealed to, is willing to free the man if you and 999 other men will work one hour each week for one year. If only 600 of the 999 men do the work, and the prisoner is executed, you will not feel much responsibility for the killing, whether you have done your _work_ or not. But if _all_ of the 999 do their work, and you neglect to do yours, you will feel entirely responsible for the death of the prisoner (assuming, of course, that the tyrant's word can be trusted).

On the other hand, suppose that the tyrant has agreed to free the prisoners if either _you_ or any _one_ of the 999 others does the work. If _no one_ does the work, and the man is executed, you yourself will feel personally responsible for the killing (and so will each of the 999 others). In this case your own independent action will save the life of the prisoner, whereas in the other case 1000 men must act.

There is a great difference between these two kinds of responsibility. Let us assume that the tyrant's conditions are _not_ met and the prisoner is executed. In the first case, whether or not you feel responsible for the killing depends entirely upon what _others_ have done. In the second case, whether or not you feel responsible for the killing depends entirely upon what _you_ have done. In the first case, your action alone could not save the man; in the second case, it _could_.

Since we have little control over the actions of others, the first kind of responsibility doesn't impress us very much, but the second kind of responsibility is <u>inescapable</u>. I will try to show you that your responsibility for most of the world's troubles today is of this second kind. That is to say, the mess we are in today is your fault, <u>entirely</u> your fault and <u>exclusively</u> your fault — because it was entirely within your power, <u>as an</u> <u>individual</u> to prevent it!

Kitselman. I really think you've gone off the deep end, this time! But go on — this, I've got to hear.

Bear with me, sir. I am not trying to tell you something new, but rather to point out some things you already know. First of all, do you feel that life as we know it is in special danger at this time?

Yes, I do. I think that people all over the world are deeply concerned about the threat of atomic war.

But surely, sir, wars have been going on since time memorial. Is there any 'special danger' in that?

There is now, because exceedingly powerful weapons have made war impractical. A fight between two men may be a practical way of settling a dispute, so long as the weapons use permit the victor to survive, but if the weapons used are such that using one of them will kill both men, then single combat, is not practical; it becomes double suicide. If the weapons used are such that not only the two combatants but everyone else in town are killed, then single combat becomes something that cannot be permitted in inhabited areas.

In a similar way, the leading nations of the world now have weapons so terrible that war is not only impractical, it has become something which cannot be permitted. We all worry about it because our lives are at stake, and perhaps the existence of civilization itself!

But these are pacifist ideas sir! There have always been people who want to outlaw war, but their ideas are not taken very seriously. I have known men who felt the need to get drunk and get into a fight every so often, just in order to 'blow off steam', so to speak. Isn't this a natural human trait? Don't you suppose that wars are waged for similar reasons? What will happen to the world if nations aren't allowed to 'blow off steam' in the age-old way?

I don't know, except that it might still <u>be</u> here. If 2 men want to fight, I may not think they are very bright, but, as far as I am concerned, let them fight — provided it is managed in such a way that no one else is hurt. If two nations want to fight, I feel pretty much the same way about it. So I don't think I'm exactly a pacifist. Nevertheless, I don't think that nations at war care much for rules.

In other words, you would be content to outlaw certain kinds of weapons and fighting.

Yes, but I do not see any likelihood of international co-operation or good faith in putting such a plan into effect.

We can say, then, that you know what you are willing to settle for, but know no way to achieve it?

Yes.

And you still feel that war between the leading nations of the world might be fatal to us all?

Yes.

What, may I ask is 'war'?

'War' is physical conflict between nations.

And what, sir, is a 'nation'?

So far as war is concerned, a 'nation' is a government and what it governs.

And what is a 'government'?

A 'government' is an organization controlling a nation — or at least trying to control a nation. If we think of a nation as a person, the government of that nation may be thought of as the ego of that person. Some egos are strong; others are weak.

Sir, what is an 'ego'?

I think my 'ego' is that part of my mind which thinks I am of special importance which is devoted to me and preoccupied with me.

Is the ego intelligent?

I don't think so, really. An ego maybe learned, skilled, all-powerful, but it is always biased and therefore never wise. As a person becomes truly intelligent, what we call 'ego' seems to vanish. Wise and creative persons seem to express themselves intelligently and effectively without any ego showing.

How many kinds of governments exist in the world today?

H'm. Three, I would say.

What three?

Monarchies, dictatorships, and democracies.

What is a 'monarchy'?

'Whoever ruled yesterday rules today; or, if yesterday's ruler is dead, his heir rules today.' A government operating on this principle is a monarchy. In this sense, no leading nation of the world today is a monarchy.

What is a 'dictatorship'?

'The most forceful man rules'. A government operating on this principle is a dictatorship. The 'force' manifested by the rule is physical only in the most primitive groups; usually it is mental and emotional. Many modern nations are dictatorships.

What is a 'democracy'?

'Let each of the People have one vote; we shall be ruled by whoever is the People's choice'. A government operating on this principle is a democracy. In this case, the ruler is chosen by the average voter. Many modern nations are democracies.

And monarchies, dictatorships and democracies are the governments which make up the world?

Yes

And among governments now existing in the world you do not see any likelihood of international co-operation or good faith?

Not so far as the minimum safety of the human race is concerned.

Then the existence of these 3 kinds of government is a major cause of our present troubles?

It must be!

Do you consider monarchy to be a sound form of government?

No, I don't.

Why not?

Because monarchy consists in letting someone else do the governing; people who live under a true monarchy have abandoned their responsibilities completely — at least insofar as the controlling of their nation is concerned. Even if there happens to be a very wise king, unless he is able to educate his subjects to adopt some better form of government, when the wise king dies, trouble begins.

You mentioned that the government of a nation is like the ego of a person. What kind of person does the monarchy resemble?

A person who thinks in exactly the same way day after day until the particular method of thinking breaks down and amnesia occurs, and who then thinks in a way different from the preceding, but in this same new way day after day until it breaks down and another amnesia occurs, and so on — such a person has an ego which resembles the government of a monarchy. It is like a series of crystallized points of view.

Sir, have you ever done anything to help establish or support a monarchy?

No, I haven't — at least, not to my knowledge.

If this is so, you cannot be blamed for the existence of monarchies in the world. Do you consider dictatorship to be a sound form of government?

No.

Why not?

Because it involves compulsion. Not only does a dictator use force and compulsion on its people, but he himself is compelled to act in certain ways in order to remain in power and alive. I like the Chinese description of being in a position of power as 'riding the tiger'. They say, "He who is riding the tiger must go where the Tiger is going" and "He who rides the tiger dares not dismount".

Both kings and dictators deny people any responsibility in government, but this is more dangerous for dictators, since they stir their people up, and people who are stirred into action are quite likely to develop a desire for responsibility. Responsible people do not submit to kings or dictators.

What kind of person does a dictatorship resemble?

A compulsive person — the kind of person who cannot help being greedy or violent or dogmatic or active or alcoholic, as the case may be. Such people don't usually live very long.

Sir, have you ever done anything to help establish or support a dictatorship?

No, I don't think I have.

If you haven't, you cannot be blamed for the existence of dictatorships in the world. Do you consider democracy to be a sound form of government?

Yes, I do.

Why?

Because, in a rational way, it tries to consider everyone, to take everyone into account. Also, a government which is based upon the opinion of the average voter is of course more stable than a monarchy or a dictatorship, because the average voter does not die, whereas kings and dictators are mortal. People who live in a democracy are governed by themselves.

Then you feel that democracy is a better form of government than monarchy or dictatorship?

Yes, I do.

If this is so, why do monarchies and dictatorships continue to exist?

I don't know. Aren't they gradually disappearing?

Monarchies — that is, true monarchies, not 'constitutional' monarchies, which, for the most part, are democracies — seem to be slowly disappearing. Dictatorships appear to be increasing, while democracies are just about holding their own.

Well, is it that democracies are relatively new and will prevail in time?

No, democracies have been with us for several thousand years at least, and dictatorships (which used to be called 'tyrannies') have always given them stiff competition.

In that case, it seems inescapable that democracies aren't much more effective than dictatorships, doesn't it?

Sir, let me ask you this: if the only governments in the world today were democracies, would you feel that the human race is 'safe', in terms of the 'minimum' safety you mentioned?

No, I don't think so. Democracies are less likely to go to war (at least, with each other) than are dictatorships, but not enough 'less likely' to suit me! And even if I thought a world consisting only of democracies would be safe enough — we don't <u>have</u> such a world! And if democracies aren't able to surpass dictatorships far enough to make them 'go out of business', so to speak — well, we're all in trouble!

What kind of person does democracy resemble?

The kind of person who listens to what everyone has to say, gives equal consideration to each opinion, averages all points of view and then acts accordingly.

Sir, have you ever done anything to help establish or support a democracy?

Yes, I have.

Then, since democracy is not good enough to rid the world of dictatorships and monarchies, in helping to establish or support democracy, sir, haven't you also helped to support dictatorship and monarchy.

I see that I have. But what else could I do?

Has it not occurred to you, sir, that if monarchy, dictatorship and democracy are not good enough to cope with the world's problems, it is necessary to find some form of government that is good enough?

But I am no expert in government!

Do you see clearly that our existing forms of government are unable to solve the problem?

Yes! I see that very clearly.

Then, sir, you are more expert in government than most of those who have earned their living at it.

But what could be better than a good democratic government? I see that monarchy and dictatorship are not good forms of government, and I see <u>why</u> they are not good. I also see that democracy as a system of government is not able to cope with the present world situation, but I don't see what is wrong with it!

Once upon a time there was a democratic shoemaker who went from town to town. He would contract to make shoes for an entire town, and his prices were very reasonable. He always collected payment in advance, so that he could buy his materials. Then he would measure the feet of every citizen, note down the measurements, and make the shoes. He made the shoes quickly and efficiently, delivered them to the townspeople and went on his way. Some people found that their shoes were too big, others found theirs too small, but many were perfectly satisfied. Those who could not wear their shoes soon gave them to those who could, sometimes receiving something in exchange. Few of the people ever realized that all of the shoes were exactly the same size, and only the shoemaker knew that he had taken all the measurements, considering them carefully and taking everyone into account, before making the shoes in the size which would fit the largest portion of the population.

In my opinion, the shoemaker was something of a scoundrel, even if you <u>do</u> call him 'democratic', because he didn't give individual consideration to his customers. But what has this to do with democratic government? Are you suggesting that democracy consists in requiring everyone to wear the same size?

Yes I am. Isn't everyone in a democracy required to wear the same size voting-power? And isn't this an insult to those who are wise, and a hopeless burden to those who are foolish? Doesn't it please only those who are neither wise nor foolish, but more-or-less average? And, like the shoemaker whom you consider a scoundrel, doesn't it fail to give individual consideration to voters?

Ouch! But even if this is so, who is to say who is wise and who is foolish?

According to you, persons who incline toward monarchy or dictatorship are foolish. If they vote, they will vote as they did yesterday, or for whoever seems strongest. Yet the scoundrelly shoemaker called 'democracy' gives these people the same size voting power as he gives those who consider all viewpoints and try to vote intelligently. To follow out your thoughts, wise persons are those who see the futility of all three forms of government in the present world crisis. If they vote, they will vote intelligently, but they probably won't see any point in voting at all. Thus the wise people let their votes go by default to those who think democracy (or dictatorship or monarchy) can solve the world's problems, and the foolish people, who cannot think for themselves, give or sell their votes to whoever rules them.

So that democracy consists in government by the average and the foolish — with the wise abstaining?

Fundamentally, yes; but in practice a democracy is governed by persons who are elected by the average and the foolish and perhaps a few of the wise. Such people are sometimes called 'the People's Choice' and they are occasionally (but not often) a little wiser than the average voter.

Well, is it so very bad to be governed by 'the People's Choice'?

No — at least not in matters the average voter can understand. But when the matter being considered is anything deeper, democracy has done (and can do) horrible things.

Such as…?

Socrates was condemned to death by a democratic vote. Pontius Pilate allowed the people of Jerusalem to choose which of the two convicted criminals he would set free, the leader of an obscure religious cult, or a popular bandit; they chose the bandit. The world has long regretted these two decisions, but they were 'the People's choice'. And it is no use objecting that more modern voting methods would have changed things, for the average voter always votes for what he can understand and against what he cannot understand. In a sense Jesus and Socrates are executed every day in a democracy. Later, of course, it is regretted, but the fact remains that the principal differences between a wise man and an average man is that the wise man understands today what the average man will *understand tomorrow. The wise man has insight; the average man has hindsight; the foolish man has neither. The wise man knows no more than the average man will come to know — but he knows it <u>now</u>. Even assuming that the foolish voters cancel each other out, the average voter can elect a wise man only by accident, because, being average, he is neither wise nor foolish. Normally he will elect someone who has qualities he understands, such as looks, vitality, charm, superficial intelligence and skill in speaking, romantic appeal, sentimental appeal, dramatic manner, etc., etc. Barabbas is the People's Choice.*

I'm beginning to see why democracies are not solving the world's problems. Nevertheless, democracy still seems good to me <u>in principle</u>. Since it doesn't work well in practice, it must be based upon a fallacy. Please show me.

Well, monarchy may be said to be based upon the principle 'do what is done — don't do what is not done'. The fallacy in this is that we get our ideas about what is and is not 'done' out of the past, so the thinking of this kind never catches up with the present or faces the future. Similarly, dictatorship is an expression of 'might is right', an idea which gets many things done — mostly foolish. Democracy in its turn is based upon the childish notion that wisdom resides in the average of all opinions. The basic idea is excellent — that a good government considers the opinions of each person — and it is true that the average cannot be obtained without knowledge of <u>all</u> the items being average, but to use all known opinions informing an average is to use them in the <u>minimum</u> <u>possible</u> <u>way</u>. In other words, if good government consists in considering everyone, democracy is the least possible form of it. Do you remember how you characterized a person who resembles a democracy?

Yes. I said such a person listens to what everyone has to say, gives equal consideration to each opinion, averages all points of view and then acts accordingly.

This certainly seems better than the person who conventionalizes instead of thinking (as a monarchy does) or the person who acts compulsively without thinking (as a dictatorship does). But the person you describe does only one kind of thinking — <u>averaging</u>. If he did any other thinking, it would occur to him before long that some people are wiser *than others, and that the opinions of wise persons should be given greater weight than the opinions of foolish persons. So the person who resembles a democracy does <u>minimum</u> thinking without ever advancing into the art of discriminating between the good and the bad, the happy and the troubled, the learned and the ignorant, the wise and the foolish. Does such a person strike you as particularly intelligent?*

I'm afraid not! The fallacy which underlies democracy, then, is the idea that people are equal in understanding.

Exactly. The world is in trouble today because it is governed by the three minimums — monarchy, which is minimum government, dictatorship, which is minimum active government, and democracy, which is minimum good government. And you, sir, are the cause of this!

Kitselman, I accept that I and millions of others, by following the rule of 'let George do it', have brought the present world crisis into being. We have been stupid and irresponsible, and we are getting exactly what we deserve. But you mean more than this don't you?

Yes, I do. I mean that you alone are responsible for the present world crisis, because you alone could have prevented it!

Frankly, I'm beginning to feel a bit frightened! Let me ask one question, please, before you go on. If you succeed in convincing me that I am the author of all the world's miseries — at least all those attributable to the three 'minimum' kinds of government — will I just have to live with it, or will there be something I can do about it?

I promise you, sir, that there will be something you can do about it. I don't think I could sleep nights if I have nothing better to do than torment people with problems which cannot be solved. I like people, for the most part; it is stupidity I do not like.

Very well, then. Now, if you please, what could I possibly have done which would have prevented the present world crisis!

I will let you tell me, so that you will realize fully that you knew enough to do it. How long have you known that democracy is based upon one vote for each person?

Ever since my early school days, I think.

And how long have you known that some people are wiser than others?

For nearly as long, I should say.

When did you come to realize that 'one vote for each person' is, in practice, a way of treating people as if all are equal in understanding?

Some years before I was twenty, certainly.

Then, at this time, you understood that 'one vote for each person' is a way of treating people as if something was so that is not so?

Yes, I did — not that I actually said it to myself, mind you — but I <u>knew</u> it.

Why didn't you do something about it?

Primarily, I guess, because I wasn't sufficiently conscious of it to look at it critically. I remember having many thoughts about the foolishness of politics and clubs and committees, all of which involved the basic realization that the 'one vote for each person' method is ridiculous, but I never <u>did</u>

anything except maybe <u>talk</u> a bit. Anyway, what could I have done?

Did you ever belong to any club or organization which operated according to the rules of 'parliamentary procedure'? Or could you have joined such a group, if you had wanted to do so?

Of course! Do you mean that I could have made use of the 'one vote for each person' procedure in order to improve on it? But how...?

You tell me.

Oh, I suppose I could have made a motion that a committee be formed to look into the basic principles of parliamentary procedure and try to find ways of improving it.

Yes, but such a motion might not be attractive to the average voter. If you can, sir, think of a strategy that would be more likely to win majority approval.

Well, I could have asked for a show of opinion, 'yes' or 'no', on the statement "some people are wiser than others". I think an overwhelming majority would vote 'yes' on this.

Excellent! Then what could you have done?

I could have asked for a vote on the question "Is it true that the principle of 'one vote for each person' does not take advantage of the fact that some people are wiser than others, and that, if we knew who they were, giving extra votes to wiser people would improve the effectiveness of our organization?"

No doubt the majority would vote 'yes' to that. What would you have done next?

I could have said "When we elect officers, we are selecting persons whom we consider to be somewhat wiser than the average of our group; this indicates that we already feel we are competent to estimate the wisdom or foolishness of another person. This being so, I move that we vote to determine whether each and every one of us is above or below average in general wisdom and good sense, and that, when this is done, or persons who are voted to be above average shall henceforth exercise two votes each in all deliberations of this organization."

All right — suppose that you have done this much. What do you think would have followed?

I imagine that, sooner or later, perhaps after much discussion, the motion would have been put into effect.

But do you think people would like being voted 'below average'?

No, of course they wouldn't. But suppose it were decided beforehand that the results of the voting would not be made public, and that only the parliamentarian or those in charge of counting votes would know whether a given voter was exercising one vote or two. It seems to me that in this way the method would work effectively without any feelings being hurt.

That seems logical. Suppose that all this had been done in the way you suggest. Would the method establish itself further?

I think so. It seems likely that before long the method would have been extended so that persons considered as being in the wisest third of the group would have 3 votes apiece, and so on.

And if you had done this, do you think the method would have spread and grown — or do you think it would have accomplished little?

Well, of course I might have had to try two or three times to get some such method into operation, but it is so simple and practical that it would certainly have been adopted eventually, and I imagine other organizations would start using it — if only for the sake of efficiency.

If the method had gone this far, do you think it would have spread into government?

I don't see how it could fail! Any genuine improvement in parliamentary procedure, even if it first appeared in a school organization, or a club, would soon spread into civic groups, business institutions and governmental bodies. I can see it penetrating into city, county and state structures, and, eventually, into the national government.

Would it stop there?

No, because if one nation had found a better form of government, other nations would want it, too — so the entire world would have been affected. Obsolete forms of government would probably have disappeared by now, at least for the most part, and we would not have the present world crisis!

Now, sir, you have outlined what you yourself thought many years ago, and what you might have done about it. What you say you could have done is simple and easy to understand; it certainly seems reasonable that <u>you could have done it.</u> Even if you have been seriously crippled in your ability to express yourself and plan parliamentary strategy, it seems to me that any kind of dogged insistence, on the importance of 'some people are wiser than others' would have caused any half-way intelligent 'one vote for each person' organization to work out and use some methods such as you have described. I also think that you are correct in saying that such a method would have spread and affected the world. This being so, is it or is it not true that the present world crisis is entirely due to <u>your</u> neglect of something which <u>you</u> understood <u>at the time</u> and which <u>you could have done</u>?

Yes, it is true.

And since <u>you alone</u> could have done it, is your responsibility reduced in any way by the fact *that others (Kitselman included) are equally responsible?*

No, it is not. It doesn't matter about others being responsible; I am responsible!

Would you like to make a formal statement of your responsibility in this matter?

Yes, I would. The present world crisis was caused by me. Most of the world's troubles were caused by me. Others are equally guilty, but that does not concern me. My guilt does not depend upon others, because by myself I could have prevented the present crisis. I knew what was wrong but I was too lazy and irresponsible even to think of doing anything about it. I saw that our systems of government are stupid, but I did not see that it was my own stupidity which kept such governments in existence. I did not see, because I did not look. I once thought that the world is not affected by my actions, but I see now that my stupidity and laziness are the direct cause of a danger which threatens to destroy our entire world and what little civilization we have. I do not know how many millions of people will die because of this stupidity of mine, but I do know that the stupidity was mine, the responsibility is mine and the guilt is mine. It is beyond measuring!

Welcome, brother! Now that you see yourself as the perpetrator of more evils than you could count, now that you realize you have been the arch-enemy of the human race, now that you know yourself to be a scoundrel beyond all imagining — it is time for you to understand that you are not alone in your depravity. There are a few of us — just a few, but more than you might expect — who recognize and acknowledge our responsibility for the troubles of the world.

Well, misery loves company, I suppose, but I can't see any satisfying basis for 'good fellowship' in such a group. Excuse me if I am a bit blunt, but I am not feeling very well at the moment, and you seem altogether too damned cheerful to suit my taste!

Sir, I beg your pardon. It is natural for you to feel pretty low at this point, because you have just accepted maximum responsibility for the state of the world. But there is another side to such responsibility, and this is the realization that, just as you <u>caused</u> the trouble, it <u>may</u> be possible for you to <u>cure</u> it! It is this that makes us cheerful. For we now know that there is something we can <u>do</u>.

Well, if you know something that will cheer me up —
now is the time, Kitselman, tell me! I feel like the
Ancient Mariner with the albatross around his neck,
and I'm damned if I can whip up any enthusiasm
about joining Parliamentary organizations and making
a nuisance of myself — if that is what you are going
to suggest!

*Oh, no — that would be far too slow for us now.
We are going about things in a more modern
way, because there is so little time. Also, very
few of us are interested in the technicalities of
voting systems, whether Parliamentary or
otherwise. So our 'method' involves the best
statistical techniques and makes use of an
electronic computer. As accurately as we can,
we combine estimates in such a way as to
obtain the wisest possible answers to questions
of all kinds, such as "what is sound
knowledge?" (in a given field), "what is the
best policy?" (in a certain matter), "how
reliable is so-and-so?" (or how trustworthy,
conscientious, personable, self-reliant,
etcetera.) — In short, we determine wise
opinion on all subjects. These standard
measures are the basis of all our activities; we
find out what to do, and then do it.*

All that sounds sensible enough. I can see how an increasing demand for accurate information on services, products, people, policies and ideas will make the 'method' better and better known. And I can see how the information itself will improve the effectiveness of business, government and education. It is a good plan, and I have no objection to any part of it — but I do not think that it will interest a sufficient number of people soon enough. I simply do not have faith in the average man's ability to judge an idea on its merits and then act on it.

Nor do I, sir. I think the average man is capable of recognizing that our 'method' is rational and possibly practical, but, in the absence of any pressure, he won't do anything else about it. However, there is pressure which is acting on all of us — at least, on nearly all of us. I call it 'the Volcano'.

And what, sir, is this 'Volcano'?

It is the pressure of the intolerable. You see, the situation we have been discussing is known to almost everyone; the world crisis is no secret. A few of us understand what it is all about, but nearly all of us are emotionally or subconsciously disturbed by what is happening and by what _may_ happen. On some level, everyone is conscious of the growing threat to life and civilization. It is an internal condition of 'alarm', and it governs us in many ways. As with steam pressure building up in a boiler, there _must_ be some escape; the Volcano _has to_ erupt. The pressure bursts out in one or more of three kinds of action — transcendental, rational and irrational. Transcendental action consists in becoming so perfectly balanced (or integrated or enlightened or saintly or emancipated or whatever you want to call it) that you can look upon the destruction of the entire world with perfect equanimity; thus you _transcend_ the problem. Rational action is what we have been talking about; being sane (if not saintly) you do the best you can to help solve the problem. Irrational action is neither sane nor saintly; not understanding the problem correctly, you do something foolish which makes you feel _as if_ you were doing something effective. There are people who are helping us because they know that if they do not do something sane or saintly (and they don't feel very saintly), they will do something _insane_. Rational action is their safety valve.

Do you mean that some people are helping you because otherwise they might find themselves joining some extremist movement, or collecting guns hysterically, or taking to drink or some other form of escapism?

Yes, exactly. These people feel a great relief at having found something sane that they can do; they are with us, not out of altruism or deep comprehension or high motives, but simply for their own peace of mind. It seems very human to me; being useful is more satisfying than being silly or stupid.

I agree; doubtless many people will be drawn to your work to experience a sense of well-being that is lacking in the un-sane and un-saintly. If it 'feels good', it will become very popular, and anything which relieves pressure feels 'good'. But tell me more about the pressures which govern us; I want to understand the 'Volcano'.

All right; let us consider some of the things we have talked about — but this time in terms of emotional and subconscious reactions. In this way we can take inventory of some of the pressures which make up the Volcano.

Proceed! I'm already beginning to see something you mentioned a moment ago — that we sense and feel many things which we do not necessarily understand. So I suppose that nearly everything we have discussed is sensed or felt by practically everyone — regardless of whether or not it is understood.

Yes, that seems to be so; it is surprising how many things we know without knowing that we know them. People know that there is a world crisis, and that it is different from any we have had before. We feel that we are in danger, and we are frightened. People know that Science is not helping the situation — in fact, many feel like blaming Science for the whole mess. People know that Business is no wiser than Science in solving the problem; there is little respect for either. People feel that the business world is exciting but corrupt, and that the scientific world is pompous, stuffy and dead. So far as emotional and subconscious reactions are concerned, Science (and Religion, too, for that matter) is regarded as if it were a true monarchy, a dead culture where tradition is king; business is regarded as if it were a world of dictatorships — active, exciting, dangerous and bad. These images are to be found in our entertainment — books, plays, radio, television, etc. — all of which cater to the emotions and the subconscious (and only secondarily to the understanding). Another aspect of our entertainment is a strong indication of how people feel about Government; I refer to the tremendous popularity of stories and dramas about law officers, adventurers, criminals and courtrooms.

What does this indicate?

Consider the plight of the average citizen in any country. He has no real voice in deciding how things shall _be_ in his town, state or country. In a monarchy or dictatorship he has no voice at all; in a democracy he is indifferently granted an infinitesimal voice — a voice so small that it has no observable effect. His government grants him the power to decide whether or not to break the law and how to manage his own affairs and family, and _that is all_ — this man who may be able to decide a thousand things intelligently, things of value to everyone. His government is very much interested in his money and his ability to shoot a gun or stop a bullet, since governments need money and guns and bullets whenever they

mismanage things too far. But does this man's
government have any use for his responsible
decisions, his power of judgement his sense of
right and wrong, practical and impractical,
wise and foolish?

No — at least, not as a citizen. I don't know why I
didn't see it before — governments have complete
contempt for the intelligence of the average citizen!

So what does the citizen do? He feels rejected,
unwanted and unappreciated — at least
outside of the circle of his family and friends
— and he finds an antidote for this
uncomfortable feeling by identifying with some
hero who is a man of decision, whose opinions
mean something, whose word is decisive and
final. Such a person is the law-man, the
adventurer, the secret-service agent, the
criminal and the judge. If no one wants me to
use my brain, if I feel that I really have no say-
so about anything, I will make myself feel
better by pretending I am someone else,
someone who enjoys, perhaps in an
exaggerated degree, the importance which I
feel should be mine. Or I comfort myself by
reading or listening to or watching some
comedy about some poor wretch who is made to

appear to be even more of a non-entity than I am. Or I enter a contest or quiz show of some kind so that the whole world can see what my government doesn't give a damn about — that I can answer a question, and speak when spoken to.

Yes, I know the feelings of which you speak. But does the average man have the right to feel that he should be consulted by his government?

If his government were a wise government, it would consult him out of wisdom, to allow him to say what he thinks and to find out what he wants. Even if it didn't, it wouldn't matter much, because the average man would feel that his government was much wiser than he. But the governments we now have all make mistakes which the average man can see, and it is apparent to him that the government is no wiser than he is — so he feels that he could be useful, but is not used. The real proof that our leaders are no wiser than the average citizen is that the average citizen can see that the leaders make the wrong decisions about half of the time. The passengers in a well-driven car can relax and enjoy the scenery; they become conscious of the driving only when it is poorly done.

That's true, I think. Of course even a wise government couldn't please everyone; some people will always be malcontents. But at present it seems to me that a large majority of the citizens in any country are actively dissatisfied with the way things are being 'run'; with present governments, discontent seems to be the rule, rather than the exception. As I think about all this I find myself amazed that I and all the other people in the world have put up with such childish forms of government for so long. How could we have been so stupid?

Shall I make an excuse for us? It cannot be on the ground that no one gave us the right idea, because Socrates said very plainly that, until we are governed by those who value understanding, the individual and the state will always have trouble, and we will not see the wonderful world we all hope for. But I can make an excuse of sorts, which is that the vote-counting and secrecy precautions involved in a 'method' (such as you say you might have started) are pretty complicated, as opposed to the 'one vote for each person' procedure, and that the more modern 'method' which we are now using could not very well have appeared in the world before the development of statistical mathematics and electronic computers. Nevertheless, if we had wanted to make a better form of government, we could have done so. Being guilty myself, I cannot explain why we didn't.

Thank you, I feel a little better now — but, as you say, we <u>could</u> have solved the problem, if we had wanted to. I approve of what you're trying to do, and I would like to help. In fact, I think many people will want to help.

Consider carefully, sir; this is no enterprise for a prudent man. If you choose to associate yourself with our activity, you can expect to encounter much argument and opposition and unpleasantness.

But you are trying to make a better world! Who on earth would oppose such an undertaking?

Everyone who has a crystallized point of view will oppose it, for we are trying to bring wisdom into business, education and government, and there are thousands of people who think that some 'ism' is wiser than wisdom. Nearly *everyone who is compulsive will oppose it, for compulsiveness is foolishness and wisdom is not compulsive. Even some thinking people — those who have not yet understood that some persons are wiser than others — will oppose it. You will probably find yourself more respected if you do not associate with us; we are likely to be called many names before our work is done.*

Kitselman, how can that hurt me? You have already shown me that I am a scoundrel beyond all imagining — and now you want me to worry about being 'respectable'! To desperadoes like me, such considerations are ridiculous. What can I do to help?

That depends, sir, on the nature of your interests. Perhaps it would be a good thing if you would write to me and tell me some of your ideas about how to apply our Standard Measures. I do not write for some abstract and hypothetical 'reader', you know; I am writing in order to communicate with <u>you</u> as a <u>particular</u> <u>person</u>, and I would like to know what <u>you</u> think.

The first copies of this book which you are reading were sent to people I know personally — people who are friends of mine. Further copies were sent to friends of *their* — and friends of friends are friends. However, personal contact of this kind, whether direct or indirect, is not the important thing. All you need to know about Kitselman is that he is someone who is communicating with you in these pages — someone who *says* he wants *you* to communicate with *him*. Is it possible that he means it?

Very touching — I hear soft violins in the background. It is gratifying, though, to hear that you want from me something more than my vote. Consider it done — if the mood strikes me, I <u>will</u> write to you, provided, of course, that I have nothing else to do at the time.

Is it possible that he means it?

It is possible. Tell me, Kitselman, do you think that this 'method', these 'Standard Measures' which you propose, will actually save the human race?

Sir, I have no idea.

Why, then, do you go to all this trouble? Is it for peace of mind, like the other people you mentioned?

No – at least I don't think so. I have another reason which pushes me in this direction.

And what is that?

I call it 'the Power Secret'. If there is something which you think is the right thing to do – do it, and do not concern yourself in the least with whether it will succeed or fail. On this basis, I can get things done, such as this communication to you. How you react to it is not _my_ responsibility; it is _yours_.

End

Biography

A. L. Kitselman was born in 1914 in the Occident, although he later became an Orientalist. His parents were rich but honest. He idled away his youth reading books, listening to classical music, climbing mountains, loafing, day-dreaming and cooking up half-baked ideas. He was addicted to mathematics, astronomy, philosophy, religion and amateur radio. He squandered his inheritance trying to set up Utopian colonies. He was a trial to his parents, and his friends are somewhat confused. In his more mature years he defrauded his employers by impersonating a chemist, a physicist, an engineer, a corporation executive, and a useful citizen. After the better class of employers saw through his little game, he posed as a psychotherapist and achieved some notoriety as a lecturer on a variety of subjects (the charge that he was vaccinated with a phonograph needle cannot be substantiated). In his old age he contents himself with his two favorite hobbies — telling people how to run their business, and rushing in where angels fear to tread.

The auto-biography originally appeared inside the back cover and on the back of the book was:

The Translator's Press
5455 LA Jolla Boulevard
La Jolla, California
U.S.A.

Discover more writings by
A. L. Kitselman
overleaf

Please visit

http://www.kitselman.com

for more on the life and work of
A. L. Kitselman

and his
"Institute of Integration"

The web site also has audio lectures
by Kitselman
on the
"Classical Authorities on Integration"

Tao Teh King

Since the 1970s, the influence of oriental philosophy, in particular the Buddhist tradition, in the field of psychotherapy has been quite profound. Taoism has not had the same impact on modern psychotherapeutic models. Yet, as early as 1936, Alva LaSalle Kitselman who was, at that time, studying oriental languages at Stanford University, with a particular emphasis on Sanskrit, created his own version of the classic text of the Taoist tradition - the book of Lao Tzu entitled the *Tao Teh King*. His version of this classic was, as he said, a restatement rather than being a new translation from the ancient Chinese. After its publication, and through a chance encounter with one of the librarians at Stanford, he began to realise that Taoism and Taoist philosophy could be used as a form of therapy, specifically in the form he called 'non-directiveness' or 'non-directive therapy.'

In this new publication of Kitselman's version of the Tao Teh King and the story of his discovery will hopefully ignite a real interest in combining the wisdom of this classic Taoist text with modern psychotherapeutic methodologies.text with modern psychotherapeutic methodologies.

Hardback with over 40 black and white photographs.
ISBN: 978-0-9565803-9-9

The Time Teachers

Following a long series of successful experiments in 1933, aimed at predicting the results of a simple coin toss, A. L. Kitselman realized that human consciousness must be able to operate outside of the constraints of time and space.

Concurrent with these experiments and in the years that followed his study of the ancient teachers of philosophy and religion, such as Kakusandha, Krishna, Buddha, Lao Tzu and Jesus, convinced him that all these teachers had a deep appreciation of the capacity of human consciousness to operate outside of time and space.

In this book Kitselman outlines a unique approach to training the human mind to enhance internal integration and achieve self mastery. He draws strongly on the Theravada Buddhist tradition as outlined in the Paṭisambhidāmagga or Path of Discernment.

Paperback
ISBN-13: 978-1501038938

E-Therapy

Would you like to ..

Improve your conduct? Is there a habit you'd like to get rid of?

Experience extreme physical pleasure? Intense, ever-fresh happiness? Deep impartial calmness?

Lose the feeling of insecurity? Make an end of doubt and perplexity? Lose all sense of fear, hatred, and grief?

Become a prodigy in science, government, business, art or education? A genius in originality, mental grasp, or in understanding others? Would you like to develop supernormal powers?

Become fully integrated? To be directly aware of things (without needing to sense them or think about them)? To realize a state of being in which there is no obstruction?

These pages tell how.
with a new introduction by Suzette Kitselman

Paperback (also on kindle)
ISBN: 978-0-9565803-7-5

E-Therapy Lectures

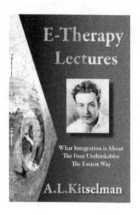

What Integration is About
The Four Unthinkables
The Easiest Way

The Institute of Integration, founded by A. L. Kitselman in the early 1950s, produced a large library of audio tapes on personal psychological integration. Kitselman felt that three of those lectures, concerning the process of integration through 'E-Therapy,' were of such significant and special interest as to warrant printing them in booklet form in 1960.

This volume faithfully reproduces those lectures—What Integration is About, The Four Unthinkables and The Easiest Way, as well as including a new introduction to her father's work by his daughter Khema Rani Kitselman.

Paperback (kindle version available)
ISBN: 978-0-9565803-8-2

If There is DYNAMITE in You Here is THE FUSE

There are two kinds of evil—doing things which should not be done, and not doing things which should be done. Many who avoid the former are guilty of the latter. This is the story of a man who avoided both. It is a true story; parts of it happened before these words were written down, other parts have happened since, and still others parts are happening now. The persons involved in the story are living at the time of this writing, and their accomplishments are as described.

A final warning to the reader:

There is no evil in this book; yet, as you read it, it may seem evil, because there are things in it which may be associated with evil in your mind. Be patient and persevere, and you will find that it is an account of actions so far from evil as to be almost incredible, and a message to you as an individual concerning your future.

Paperback
ISBN: 978-0-9927706-9-3

Printed in the USA
CPSIA information can be obtained
at www.ICGtesting.com
LVHW081155130224
771604LV00019B/52

9 780993 346538